TOP CELEBRITIES WH
THE ZIG & ZAG ANNUAL...

£4.99

D0230079

The KILLER ANNUAL from OUTER SPACE!

C-C-CONTENTS

OO-ER!

Published by
Grandreams Limited
Jadwin House, 205/211 Kentish Town Road,
London, NW5 2JU.

Printed in Italy.

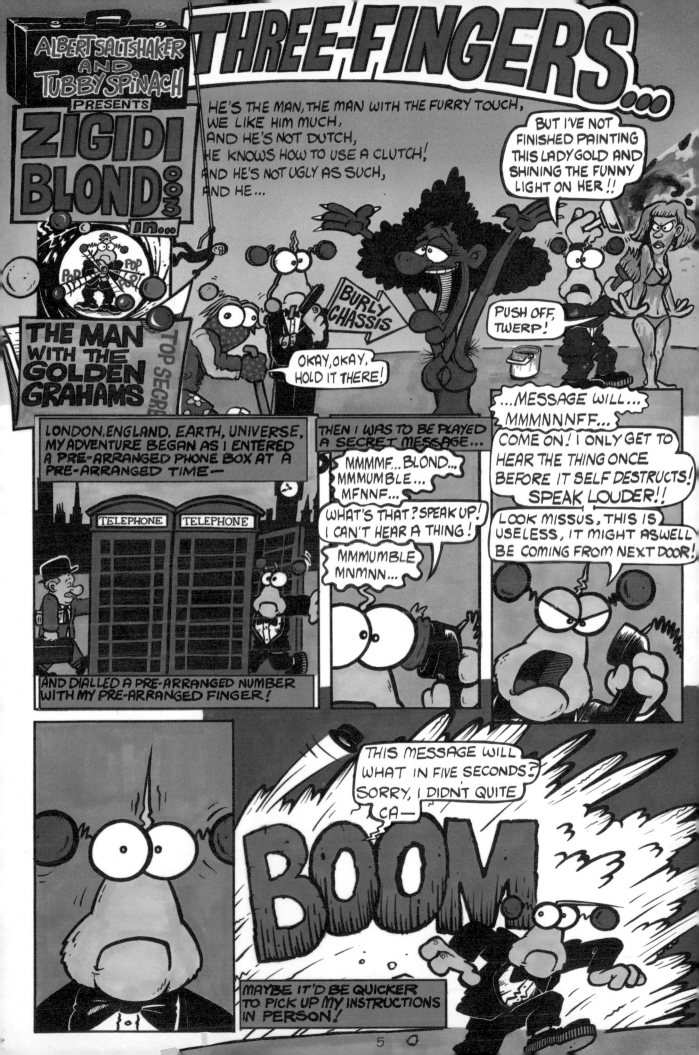

Simply insert your photo into the space marked 'Insert Head' and show it to all your friends. When they ring us up, we promise to tell them you were really there and you're our best mate ever. (NB: We can't offer this service to anyone using the photo as an alibi if they're in trouble with the law. Sorry.)

love Zig & Zag

RESPECT! MARKY MARK IS IN THE HOUSEY-HOUSE!

AND BLOW ME DOWN IF IT ISN'T OUR OLD PAL LENNY HENRY!

TWO GUYS WITH **ONE THING** IN COMMON – THEY BOTH HAVE **TWO FIRST NAMES** & NO PROPER **SURNAME**

TIME FOR ZIG & ZAG'S **TOP 10** PEOPLE WITH 2 FIRST NAMES & NO PROPER SURNAME:

10 ROD STEWART – A cross between a fishing rod & a type of tartan. And so's his name.

9 JASON DONOVAN – The best parts of Jason Priestley & Donovan Leitch, giving us old lemon head.

8 LYSETTE ANTONY – Antony, as in Hopkins, Lysette as in...er...

7 BRYAN ADAMS – Not only two first names, but one of them's spelt wrong.

6 TORI AMOS – Amos might be the bloke from Emmerdale, but Tori isn't a real name at all.

5 DIANA ROSS – One girl's name, one boy's, & a nose like Michael Jackson's.

4 ELTON JOHN – First bit borrowed from Ben Elton, last bit from John Bon Jovi, hair from the barber's floor.

3 PHIL COLLINS – We know Colin doesn't have an 's' at the end, but we like him anyway.

2 MARKY MARK – Wow! Only one name, played twice. Skill!

1 LENNY HENRY – Made from leftover bits of Lenny the Lion & Henry's Cat. Obviously.

FUNNY MR. MASHED POTATO FACE

Cut out these bits of face & add them to a bowl of mashed potato. Stir in carefully & serve to your friends.

Imagine their surprise when they come across an eyeball or a nose.

CRISP BOBBING

Just like traditional Apple Bobbing, only for people who prefer crisps (Me—Zig). Simply sprinkle a packet of your feve flavour into a large bowl of water and try to fish them out with your teeth

Better hurry up though or they'll go all soggy and you'll come up looking like a crispodite from the Planet Scabb.

PIN THE TAIL ON THE DINKY

Not nearly so boring as the usual 'donkey' game — this time you use a small die-cast model car.

Okay, you might break a few pins in the process, but anything beats getting that close to a donkey's bottom.

ZIG AND ZAG'S PARTY PIECES

BLIND MAN'S BUM

Blindfold a guest and spin them round twenty or thirty times. Then tell them to kick their own bum. He/she will fall over and you will all laugh a very lot.

Note: Don't make Zig's mistake — don't blindfold someone's bum and tell them to kick you in the face. It is not nearly so funny.

KISS CHASE

Run up to those hard men of rock, kiss, and go 'boo' very loudly.

They will run away 'cos they are sissies who wear girls make-up. Then you can chase them.

POSTMAN'S KNOCK

Wait till there's a knock on the door then take it in turns to guess whether it is the postman or not. The first person to guess correctly that it's the postman knocking wins.

Note: If you're playing at night, this can take an awful long time. Plus the postman always rings. Usually twice.

ZIG AND ZAG'S ROUGH-HOUSE GUIDE TO WRESTLING

THE INS & OUTS
THE UPS & DOWNS
THE DO'S & DON'TS
THE HAVES & HAVE-NOTS
THE FURBELOWS &
QUINNIDINGLES
THE TOPS & BOTTOMS!
oooer missus!!

FIRST — grab your brother when he's not looking, and exert the following playful holds on him:

HALF NELSON — Drag your opponent halfway up Nelson's Column — and leave him there.

ARMLOCK — Take your opponent's arm and lock it upstairs in his bedroom. Now let's see him hit you back.

GRIDLOCK — Actually, this is a name for American Football. But if your opponent's head comes off under your arm, you might as well try & get a Touchdown with it.

BOSTON HALF WHEELED POSED DONUT — Er, this one doesn't exist.

TRIPLE PIKE AND SOMERSAULT — This is actually a diving manouevre, but useful if the ring is flooded.

CLOVE HITCH — This is really a knot, but if you can tie one with your opponent's leg — you've won.

PATTA-CAKE — You & your opponent pat hands & sing "Patta cake patta cake baker's man." Then punch the referee.

REMEMBER: Wrestling can hurt a very lot, so only ever **PRETEND.** Especially when grown-ups are in the room. 'Cos a safe home is a happy home and it's all just an excuse for big men to wear leotards. So there.

16

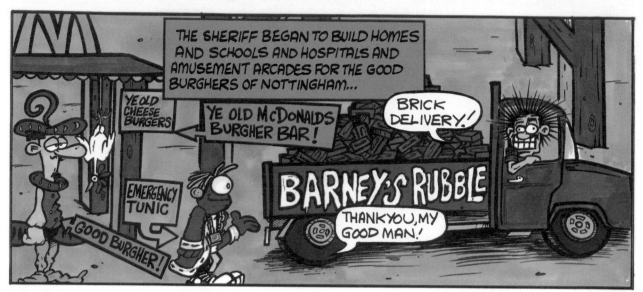

22

ZIGMUND & ZAGNATIOUS AT HOME

EXCLUSIVE FIRST PICTURES OF FLAT 4, LONDON!!!

Top celebrities, Zigmund and Zagnatious Zogly kindly allowed the cameras of WOTCHA! into their private superstar abode.

The only major comic duo to share a bed since Morecambe and Wise, Zig and Zag recreate the fateful moment they embarked on their TV career. "We did have bunk beds once but I got a nose bleed sleeping on the top! The Fire Brigade had to get me down!" says Zig (left).

A mere stone's throw from the homes of many other top TV Stars (providing you have access to a medieval siege catapult and a prevailing wind) we asked the boys to recall the early days of their career and how it was they became famous. Which of them first had the idea to go into television?

"It suddenly came to me one morning in bed after a rather heavy night out with a tour bus full of supermodels!" admitted Zagnatious. "No it did not! It was all my idea," claimed Zigmund, "I was in bed suffering rather badly with a fever brought on by an acute case of Zogabongitis at the time."

Zogabongitis, a common and devastating Zogian illness, swells the Zogabonds up to ten times their normal size, making them tender and hypersensitive to more than just normal radio signals and satellite TV transmissions. It was during this stage of his illness that Zigmund claimed he received the revelation while in telepathic communication

In 1987, the Zogly Brothers released their cult nine hour black and white Art House movie, "Bath", to no critical acclaim whatsoever. The pair were in a lather.

The exact flavour of the crisps was the subject of a heated debate during their first TV discussion programme, "Zogarama", back in 1983. Viewing figures were the lowest ever. It remains the only programme in history to be cancelled during its commercial break!

with a packet of crisps from the Willesden Green branch of Tesco's.

In the wake of this first setback the brothers split up for a while, but continued to live in the same flat, refusing to talk to each other until one day they found themselves trying to use the bath at the same time.

"I had a really hot date down at Stringfellows." recalled Zagnatious. "An' I wanted to play with my toy submarines!" declared Zigmund.

In 1987, the Zogly Brothers released their cult nine hour black and white Art House movie, "Bath", to no critical acclaim whatsoever. The pair were in a lather.

Neither was willing to give up the bath. The stalemate was only broken when Zagnatious threatened "to tell mummy!" From then on baths featured in all their work. An early version of their next TV show was called "In Yer Bath, Missus!" in which they wanted to broadcast live from baths around the country. Unfortunately the programme was due to go out on Sunday nights during peak bath-time, so they couldn't find any free baths to broadcast from. The audience drained away and the plug was pulled.

Script writing was often hampered by the fact that Zigmund frequently ate the script, while Zagnatious would often stop to compose hit songs, using his biro as an impromptu whistle.

But now, it seemed, fortune smiled on them. The theme of the bathroom ever present in their work, they changed their catchphrase to "In Yer Face, Missus!" and it wasn't long before the "The Crunch" as we know it today finally appeared. Everything worked - except the script and the Brothers spent long hours frantically writing and re-writing.

And so, as they sit painfully astride their present pinnacle of fame, we can only wonder where it will all end? At the bottom of the page probably, just about here. **W**

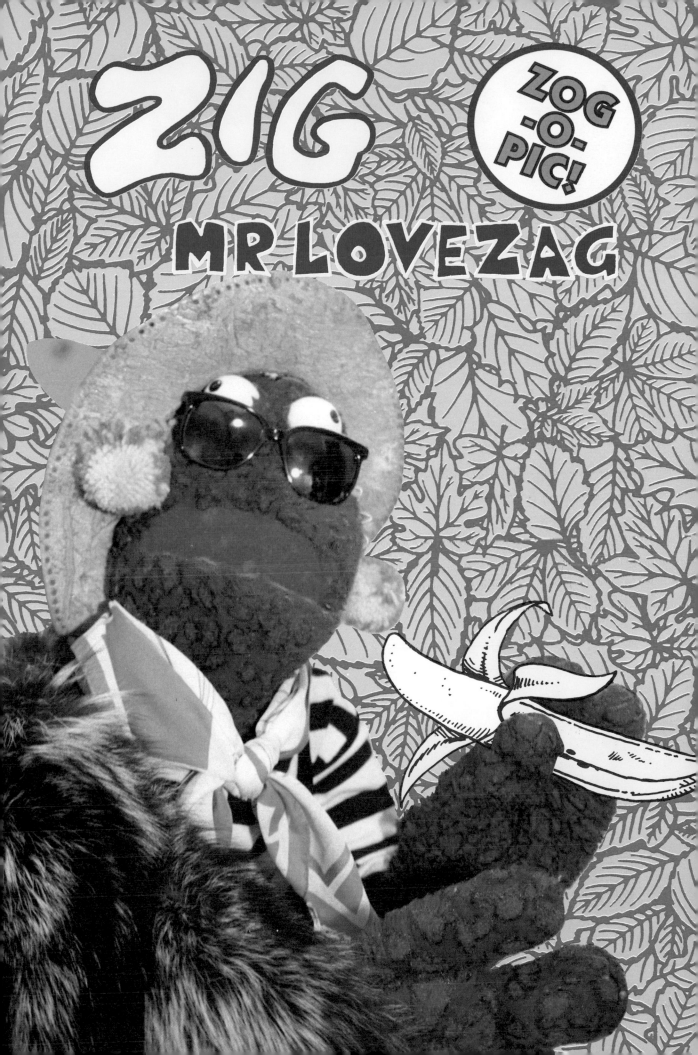

Dear Diary...

Dear Diary,
Last week I went to a showbusiness bash where I met MICHAELA STRACHAN. It was lurve at first sight. Our eyes met across a crowded room and boy was it crowded! They really tried to PACKHAM in! I thought she was REALLY WILD and it SHOWed. She thought I was an ANIMAL! I invited her back to my place where we had a great time, but the poor girl became so infatuated with me that she wanted to be just like me in every way. A hopeless task, as I'm sure you will admit.

Zogabongs – she even claimed she could pick up MTV on them! She was a really nice girl and very talented. Sad really.

It got so bad that she even pretended that she had Zogabongs. This is the last picture of us together. You can see her fake

The next day I jetted over to a Malibu beach party given by the Cruiser himself. Jack, Winona, Bruce, Jean-Claude, Cher and Robin were all there and I bumped into Jerry Hall. She was pretending to have trouble with the barbi, so I would have to go over and help her. Talk about a HOT date! We fanned the FLAMES of desire until we accidentally burned all the sausages and Clint, who was next in the queue for a burger, really did find himself IN THE LINE OF FIRE! How we all laughed about that one! I told Tom and Nicole that it was FAR AND AWAY the best barbi I had been to for ages.

WHY?

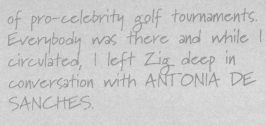

of pro-celebrity golf tournaments. Everybody was there and while I circulated, I left Zig deep in conversation with ANTONIA DE SANCHES.

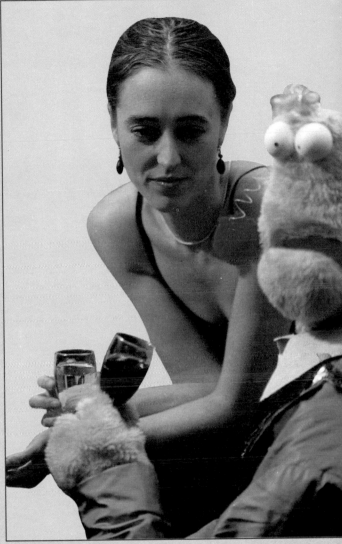

Dear Diary,
The other week I received a call from a TV company. They want to make a mini-series of my romantic exploits, based on my autobiography, "MR LOVEZAG". In it, I play myself. Here I am on set, rehearsing a scene where I get stranded on a desert island with an all-girl pop group (played by real-life pop group, GIRLFRIEND) and I have to console them by picking out nine of their records as my desert island discs. The directors asked me to use a stunt double for these scenes, but I insisted on doing the entire thing myself!

After a hard day's shooting, I went out on the town to a celebrity charity do. I do like to help those celebrities less fortunate than I — which is why I let Zig hang around. (But don't tell him that, this is between me and you, diary.) We were raising money for a golf course on which Over-the-hill Celebs can spend their twilight years on TV — in an endless round

Monday, PiCk up lawndry!

They seemed to get on very well, as they were still talking when I came back, spinning from the social whirl. Later, I asked what it was they were talking about so intently all evening. He turned to me all starry-eyed and sighed, "Toe Cheese!" I should have known!

Well, that's it for now, dear Diary. Until next time, Au Revoir!

YOU KNOW, IT'S NOT ALL BRIGHT LIGHTS AND GLAMOUR IN TV. OKAY 96% IS. BUT THAT LEAVES 4 BORING PERCENT THAT'S VERY DULL WE CAN TELL YOU, MISSUS!

BACKSTAGE PASS
ACNE
ALL AREAS

Here's us behind the scenes before we go live on air - but there's always time for **Zag** to turn on his Mr. Sexy look for a quick photo!

Here's Gaby before she puts her make-up on and her trade mark blond wig. She has the same people who did Robin Williams in Mrs. Doubtfire!

Zig is nonchalantly swotting up his script which is written in 'smell-braille' on a strip of fly paper.

Ooops! Here you see us before the dabhands from the make-up department have got to work. As you can see, **Zag's** hair is notoriously unmanageable, and this particular morning he has an historic case of **bed-head.**

As for poor **Zig**, his secret is out. Before his discreet green toupe is applied, Zigidi-bo is a shocking **ginge!** And of course he wears lenses.

33

ZIG's ZAG-TIVITY PAGE

ZIG-EYE WIGGLER

CUT OUT   CUT OUT

IT'S ZAG-MAZING

ZAGGYAGGY JONES has landed in the Valley Of The Supermodels – slap bang in The Maze of Doom! Help him find his way out to the A-MAZE-ONs!

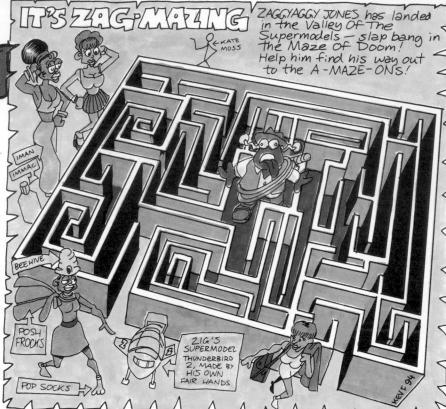

KATE MOSS

IMAN
IMMAC

BEEHIVE

POSH FROCKS

POP SOCKS

ZIG'S SUPERMODEL THUNDERBIRD 2, MADE BY HIS OWN FAIR HANDS

KEV F 94

UH-OH... BIG TOE

Zig's big toe has gone missing. Help him find it. Duh...

TOE A   TOE B   TOE C

TOADY

TOTO (OUT OF THE WIZARD OF OZ)

Have a Break, Have A QUICK SNAP!

Cut out these two cards & deal one to each player. Player one place card face up. Then player 2 does. If the two cards match, shout 'Snap.' Repeat till bedtime.

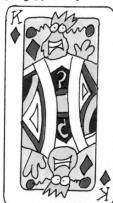

To make your own Zig-Eye Wiggler, just cut out the two eye holes along the dotted lines, and cut out the stripey strip.

Place the strip behind the eye holes & move slowly up & down. See how his eyes follow you around the room? Like so...

Fig A   Fig B

ZOGWORD BY ZAG

1	2	3
4		
5		

1 across – Universe's greatest alien
4 across – Swedish stove
5 across – Short for Gary
2 down – see 4 across
3 down – see 5 across

JOIN THE DOTS

What is Zag wearing? And why is it so uncomfortable? Join the dots to find out.

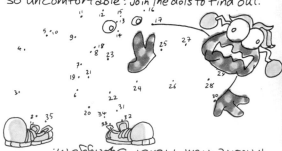

Answer: Aargh! It's the Zogian-eating Trilobite from Planet Squiggoth!

ROADMENDERS*

"DO BE DO BE DOOO BE DOOOOOO..."
Who amongst us doesn't know that now legendary theme tune? Not bloomin' many, I'll be bound. It's the theme tune to none other than Eastenders. But do you ever feel that you are watching a foreign programme with all that rhyming slang?...

"One day I was fed up with staying DUSTY, so I decided to take the old CHOCOLATE for a walk. I brushed my MARKS, put on my best COUGH, went out of the CEILING and down the PORCELAIN COMMODE. I bumped into an old TECTONIC in a BUCKET. We went for a quick KITCHEN, then took a BRIDGET through the park. I don't know where the time went, but when I got back to my CAVITY it was completely JURASSIC and my RAMSEYS were killing me, so I had a quick CAULIFLOWER and went straight up to BILL."

Confused? There's no need to be. With the aid of our Roadmender chums - Todd Carty, Susan Tully, Michelle Gayle and Danni Minogue (from the East End of Australia!) - you can begin to parlez-vous Zogney Rhyming Slang with this free introductory lesson. You'll soon be staff nursing like a good 'un - And that's no custard or your bangers back!

A BRIEF GUIDE TO ZOGNEY RHYMING SLANG

a few examples of rhyming slang:

Bridget Fonda = Wander	Stairs = Apples and Pears
Chocolate Log = Dog	Cheese Spread = Dead
M & S Underwear = Hair	Jurassic Park = Dark
Bangers 'n' Mash = Cash	Wyatt Earp = Bottom Burp
Porcelain Commode = Road	Texas Homebase = Face
Tectonic Plate = Mate	Tate & Lyle = Style
Dusty Bin = In	Bill and Ted = Bed
Poop Deck = Cheque	Cavity Wall Insulation Foam = Home
Ear, Nose and Throat = Coat	Ceiling and Floor = Door
Bucket and Mop = Shop	Kitchen Sink = Drink
Ramsey Street = Feet	Cauliflower = Shower
Staff Nursing = Conversing	Custard Pie = Lie
Polo Mint = Skint	Bicycle Pump = Chump
Polyunsaturated Fat = Hat	Cough 'n' Hack = Anorak

* Zogney Rhyming Slang for Eastenders

Once you've mastered these words try dropping them into everyday conversation!

"CAN I HAVE TWO POUNDS OF YOUR BEST STAIRS, VEGETABLE SAMOSA?"
Can I have a couple of pounds of apples and pears please, Mr Greengrocer?

"PSST! I'M SORRY, ME OLD TECTONIC, I DIDN'T WANT TO SAY THIS TO YOUR TEXAS, BUT YOU LOOK LIKE A COMPLETE BICYCLE IN THAT POLYUNSATURATED FAT!"
I'm sorry, my dear friend, but you look a right chump in that hat!

"I'M COMPLETELY CHEESE SPREAD POLO, I'VE GOT NO BANGERS, WILL YOU TAKE A POOP?"
I'm dead skint. I have no cash, will you take a cheque?

"ISN'T IT NICE TO FEEL THE WIND IN YOUR MARKS & SPENCER'S UNDERWEAR, MISSUS?"
Isn't it nice to feel the wind in your hair, madame?

If you would like to learn more about Zogney Rhyming Slang, a complete correspondence course and set of language tapes is available through ZOG ENTERPRISES, 10 ZOGLAND HEIGHTS, PLANET ZOG. Please enclose a blank poop deck.

OH NO! IT'S THE "OH NO, IT'S THE END OF THE ANNUAL!" PAGE!

BUT DON'T WORRY. IF YOU DON'T WANT THE ANNUAL TO END JUST YET, WHY NOT TURN BACK TO PAGE ONE AND START ALL OVER AGAIN?

We asked three famous people what they thought of our first ever annual. Would they swop one issue of their own Brand X annual for two copies of the Zig and Zag Annual?

"You must be joking! I've never seen such a load of old codswallop in all my life! Annual indeed. Once every hundred years is too much if you ask my opinion. I say, what are you doing with that gag ggmmmmph ffghp mmmmph..."
- Victor Meldrew,
alias Richard Wilson

← Bob

"No, I don't *($@?% think so. I mean, the best thing about this %&*$<@ annual is this bit an' that's only because it's the last %&*>?$@ page in the whole thing..."

- Sir Bob Geldof

"Well, will Mr Day, swop his annual for two Zig and Zag annuals. No, I don't think I will, thank you. You see I've always been a staunch believer in educational features myself and I think you'll find that there were proportionally more educational features per annual under the previous Labour Government, than at present. Next Question please? Yes, the lady at the back in the snot-coloured jumper and white hat..."
- Sir Robin Day

ThE eNd

SO THERE YOU HAVE IT - Never ask a bunch of grumps about your annual.